CONCEPTS

Counting & Place Value

TEACHING GUIDE

A number is an idea. A numeral is a symbol which stands for a number.

The decimal place value system is based on the number ten. The value of each of the digits in the decimal system—0, 1, 2, 3, 4, 5, 6, 7, 8, and 9—depends on its place.

This book is designed to reinforce the concepts of place value and counting typically introduced in the first grade mathematics texts. The pages are presented in a suggested order, but may be used in any order which meets the needs of an individual or a class. Second grade teachers may find the use of selected sections of the book helpful with children who need extra practice in counting and understanding place value.

The teacher should make physical objects available to the children to count and to group into tens. Manipulation of objects should precede the use of the pages in this book.

ANSWER KEY

Page 1

9
6
2
3
4
8
1
10
5
7

Page 2

3, 5, 8
1, 6, 9
2, 4, 7, 8
2, 3, 6, 7, 9
1, 2, 4, 5, 8

Page 4

fourth   first

            third

second   fifth

Page 5

third
seventh
first
sixth
eighth

tenth
second
ninth
fifth
fourth

Page 6

Riddle answer: AUTOMOBILE

Page 7

11
13
15
17
19

12
14
16
18
20

Page 8

2 tens 5 ones; 20 + 5; 25
3 tens 8 ones; 30 + 8; 38
46
50
34
35
51
28
Riddle answer: GIANTS

Page 9

6 tens 2 ones
5 tens 3 ones
28
45
74

Page 10

4 tens 7 ones	3 tens 0 ones
5 tens 3 ones	8 tens 2 ones
6 tens 8 ones	9 tens 4 ones
2 tens 9 ones	7 tens 5 ones
1 ten 6 ones	6 tens 1 one
9 tens 2 ones	2 tens 2 ones
3 tens 8 ones	4 tens 9 ones
7 tens 3 ones	6 tens 0 ones
1 ten 8 ones	5 tens 7 ones

Counting & Place Value

Page 11

Riddle: Who never gets
paid for doing a day's
work? a night watchman

Page 18

67, 77   12, 22
55, 65   36, 46
41, 51   84, 94
70, 80   73, 83

Page 19

30, 35, 42, 44, 57, 66, 73
21, 25, 43, 55, 70, 73, 82
32, 42, 58, 59, 65, 88, 89
67, 76, 85, 87, 92, 97, 99

Page 20

63 52 78
44 30 98

14 57 48
48 96 20
63

Page 21

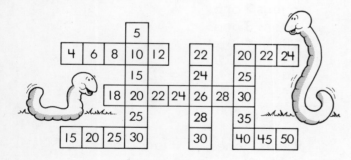

Page 24

14   12
12   14
20   16
16   20
23   19
19   23

Page 25

13¢ 35¢ 28¢ 20¢ 41¢ 17¢ 52¢

<   <   <
>   >   >
>   >   <

Page 26

5	6	7	8
50	60	70	80
60	50	40	30
25	30	35	40
23	28	33	38
80	75	70	65
10	12	14	16
42	40	38	36
11	16	22	29

Page 27

33, 43, 53, 63, 73, 83
35, 45, 55, 65, 75, 85
38, 48, 58, 68, 78, 88
32, 42, 52, 62, 72, 82
40, 50, 60, 70, 80, 90
36, 46, 56, 66, 76, 86
8, 10, 12, 14, 16, 18
7, 9, 11, 13, 15, 17
25, 30, 35, 40, 45
24, 29, 34, 39, 44

Page 28

Cross out: 50
            85
            21
             5
            29
            53
            30

                            Counting & Place Value

Count each set. Write the numeral.
Match the numeral to the word.

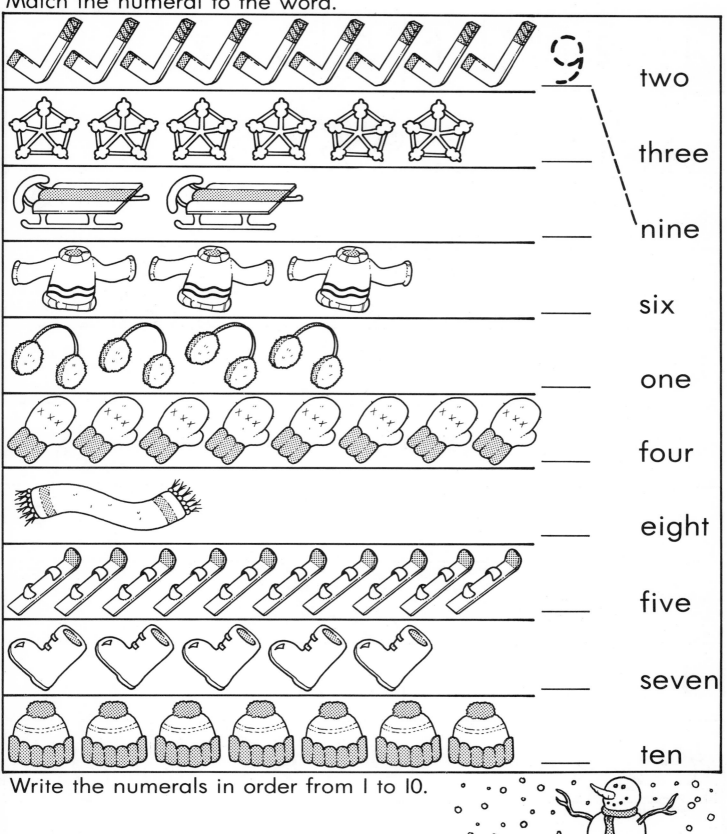

two

three

nine

six

one

four

eight

five

seven

ten

Write the numerals in order from 1 to 10.

_____ _____ _____ _____ _____

_____ _____ _____ _____ _____

1   Counting & Place Value

Write the missing numerals.

1	2	3	4	5	6	7	8	9

1	2		4		6	7		9

	2	3	4	5		7	8	

1		3		5	6			9

1			4	5			8	

		3			6	7		9

2

Counting & Place Value

What kind of "key" is good to eat?
Count the dots.
Color 1 and 2 — blue
Color 3 and 4 — orange
Color 5 — brown
Color 6, 7, and 8 — red
Color 9 and 10 — green

Answer: A turkey

3   Counting & Place Value

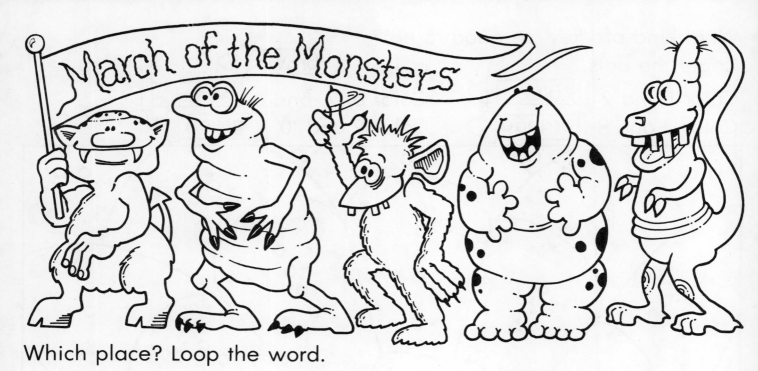

March of the Monsters

Which place? Loop the word.

second

third

fourth

first

second

third

second

third

fourth

first

second

third

third

fourth

fifth

4

Counting & Place Value

Which place? Loop the word.

	first	(third)	tenth
	seventh	first	second
	sixth	ninth	first
	fourth	eighth	sixth
	eighth	sixth	fifth

	ninth	second	tenth
	sixth	seventh	second
	fifth	ninth	eighth
	second	fifth	tenth
	fourth	seventh	ninth

5   Counting & Place Value

Match.

Cars labeled: 3rd · 1st · 2nd · 6th · 5th · 4th · 9th · 7th · 8th · 10th

What ten letter word starts with "gas"?
Write the letters on the correct blanks to find the answer. Read down.

third letter	T
fifth	M
first	A
sixth	O
second	U
fourth	O
eighth	I
seventh	B
tenth	E
ninth	L

___ ___ T ___ ___ ___ ___ ___ ___ ___

6

Counting & Place Value

Loop ten blocks to make a ten.

The blocks are put in a stack.
The stack of blocks is called "one ten."

Count the stacks and the single blocks. Record.

tens	ones
1	0

tens	ones
1	1

= 11

tens	ones

=

tens	ones

=

tens	ones

=

tens	ones

=

tens	ones

=

tens	ones

=

tens	ones

=

tens	ones
2	0

=

7   Counting & Place Value

The blocks are in stacks of ten. Count the stacks. Then count the single blocks. Record.

	Table Form	Expanded Form	Standard Form
	tens | ones 1 | 2	10 + 2	12
	tens | ones	___ + ___	___
	tens | ones	___ + ___	___

Match each set of sticks with the standard numeral.

51 G

46 S

50 A

35 T

28 I

34 N

Write the letter above the numeral. What kind of ant is the largest?

___ ___ ___ ___ ___ S
51   28   50   34   35   46

8

Counting & Place Value

Count the tens and ones on the number line.

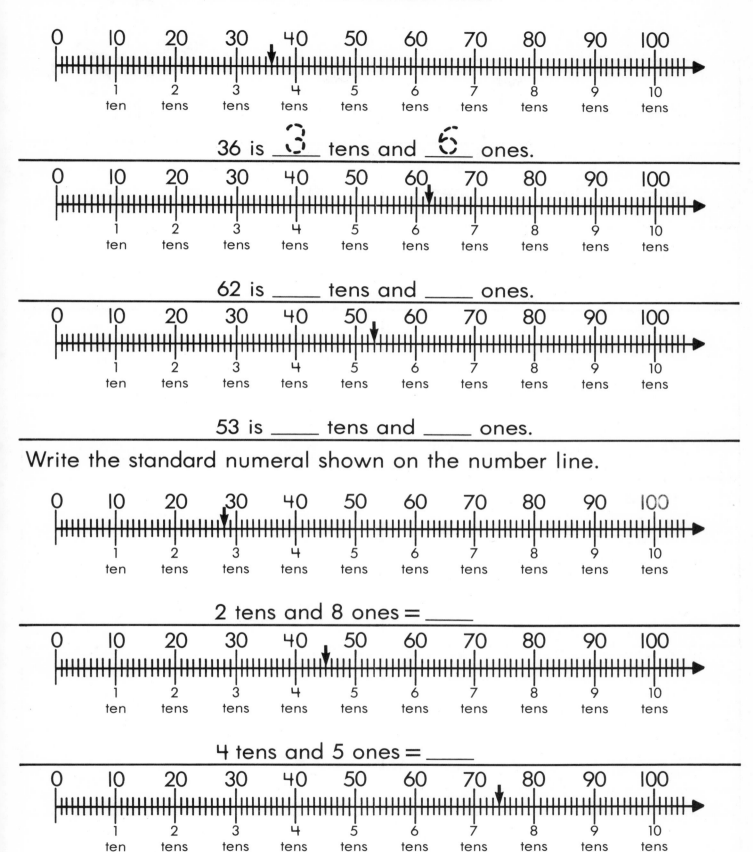

36 is ___3___ tens and ___6___ ones.

62 is _____ tens and _____ ones.

53 is _____ tens and _____ ones.

Write the standard numeral shown on the number line.

2 tens and 8 ones = _____

4 tens and 5 ones = _____

7 tens and 4 ones = _____

9   Counting & Place Value

Write the numerals that name the tens and ones.

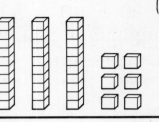

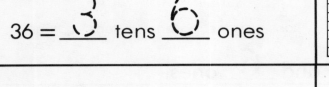

36 = __3__ tens __6__ ones

47 = ____ tens ____ ones	30 = ____ tens ____ ones
53 = ____ tens ____ ones	82 = ____ tens ____ ones
68 = ____ tens ____ ones	94 = ____ tens ____ ones
29 = ____ tens ____ ones	75 = ____ tens ____ ones
16 = ____ ten ____ ones	61 = ____ tens ____ one
92 = ____ tens ____ ones	22 = ____ tens ____ ones
38 = ____ tens ____ ones	49 = ____ tens ____ ones
73 = ____ tens ____ ones	60 = ____ tens ____ ones
18 = ____ ten ____ ones	57 = ____ tens ____ ones

 Counting & Place Value

Write the words from the expanded form boxes in the matching standard form boxes. Follow the example. You will make a riddle!

Expanded form.

20 + 1 FOR	50 + 9 A	40 + 7 GETS
10 + 6 DAY'S	30 + 4 WHO	60 + 8 A
50 + 2 NEVER	20 + 5 WORK?	80 + 3 PAID
10 + 1 DOING	90 + 2 WATCHMAN	60 + 1 NIGHT

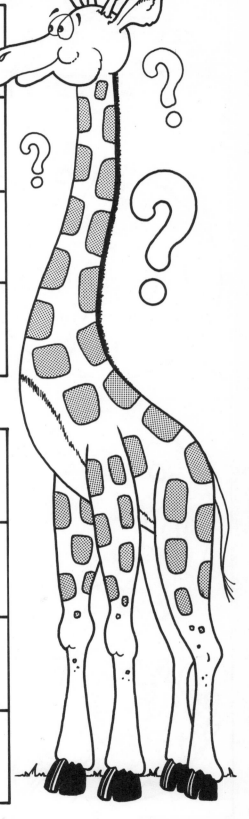

Standard form.

34	52	47
83	21 FOR	11
68	16	25
59	61	92

Counting & Place Value

Write the missing numerals.

12

Color the boxes in order from 50 to 70 to make the path for the squirrel to reach the nut. Do not go diagonally.

Begin here.

50	52	53	55	56	58	59
51	52	53	56	55	57	60
53	51	54	52	58	59	60
54	52	55	56	57	59	61
56	57	58	64	65	63	62
62	61	60	66	65	64	64
66	67	65	67	63	62	61
65	68	66	68	69	70	

End here.

13

Counting & Place Value

Complete the number lines.

73 〇 〇 76 〇 〇 〇 80 〇

91 〇 93 〇 〇 96 〇 〇 〇

〇 83 〇 〇 86 〇 〇 89 〇

Count by ones from 70 to 100. Connect the dots.

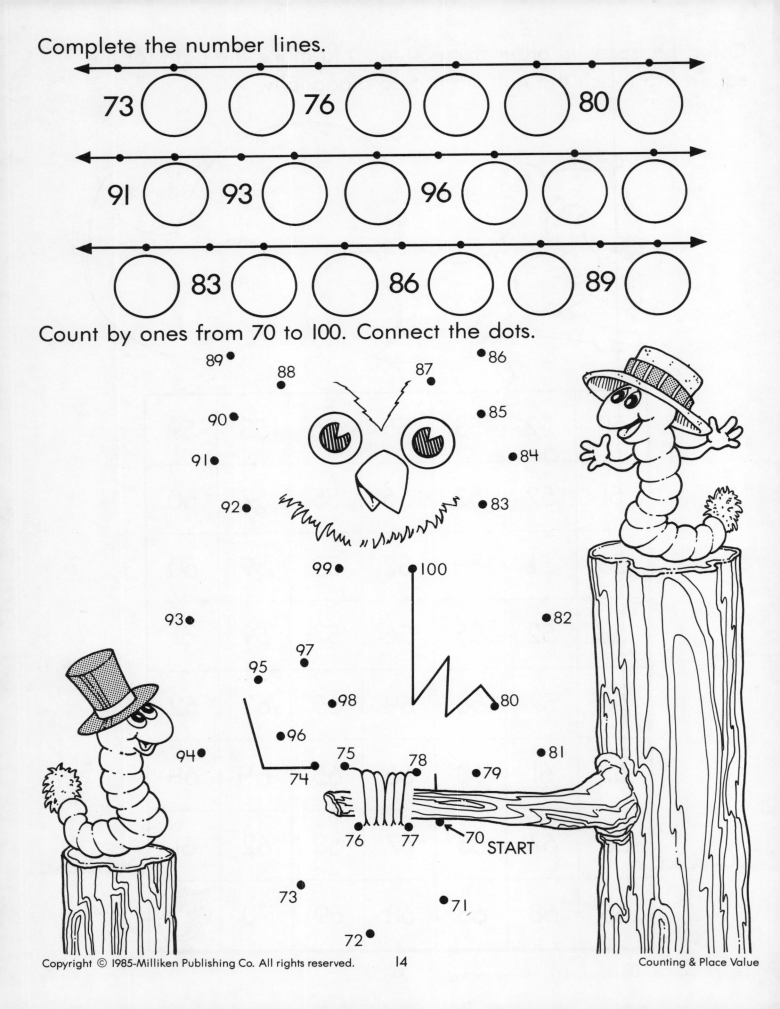

89

88   87   86

90   85

91   84

92   83

99   100

93   82

97

95

98   80

96

94   75   78   81

74   79

76   77   70 START

73   71

72

14

Counting & Place Value

Number Suzie's pennies to see how many cents she has saved.

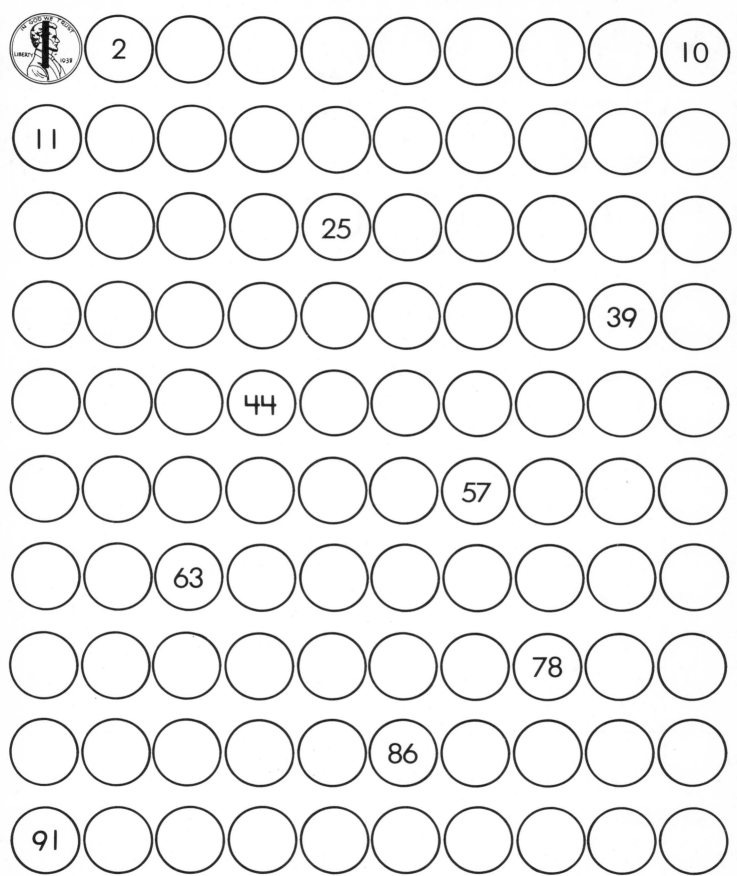

15   Counting & Place Value

Color numbers less than 50 red.
Color 50 brown.
Color numbers more than 50 blue.

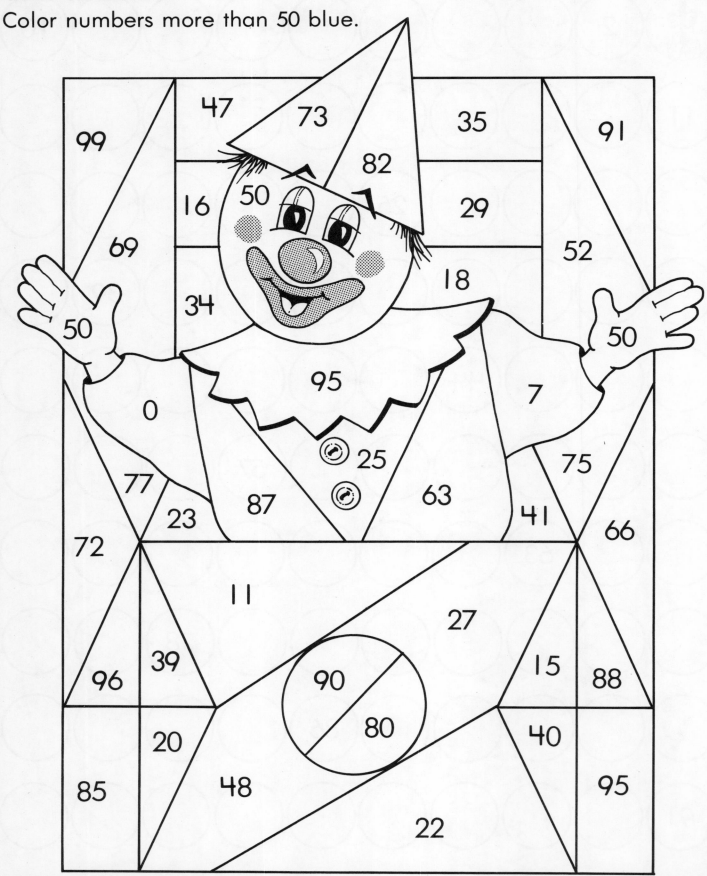

16

Counting & Place Value

Connect the ★s, counting by 10s from 10 to 100.
Connect the os, counting by 10s from 10 to 100.
Connect the +s, counting by 10s from 10 to 100.
Connect the •s, counting by 10s from 10 to 100.

40
o

o 20

60
o

50
o

30
o

30
•

20
•

10
o

+ 100

70 o

10

+ 90

40
•

80 o

100
•

90 o

50
•

60
•

90
•

+ 80

100 o

+

70
•

80
•

+ 70

10

70
•

+
30

+
50

+
60

20 +

20
★

10
★

+
40

30
★

50
★

40
★

60
★

70
★

80
★

90
★

100
★

17

Counting & Place Value

Write the number that is 10 more or 10 less on the balloons.

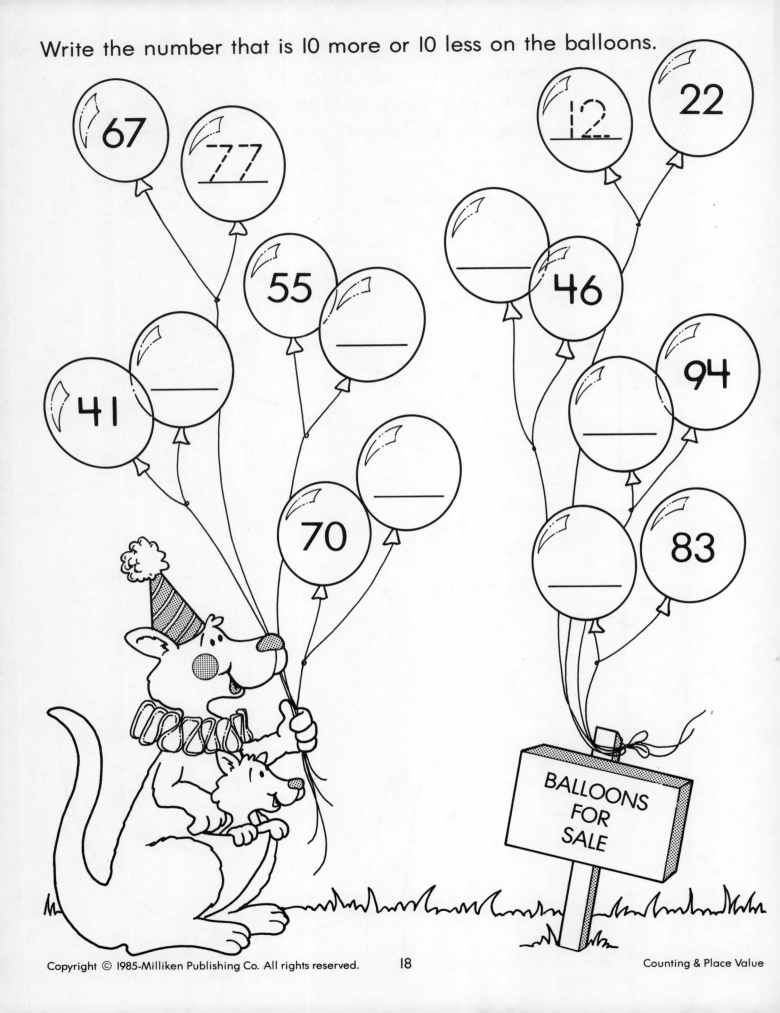

67

77

12

22

55

46

41

94

___

___

70

___

83

___

Counting & Place Value

BALLOONS FOR SALE

Write in order from least to greatest.

30   35

73

42   57

44

66

(30) ( ) ( ) ( ) ( ) ( ) ( )

25   70

82   73   21

55   43

88
32
65   59
42   58   89

92
87   97
99   85
67   76

19   Counting & Place Value

Which is more? Loop the number.

63 36

52 51

74 78

44 34

30 29

89 98

10 (12)

Which is less? Loop the number.

48 49

14 41

57 75

20 30

84 48

97 96

66 63

20

Counting & Place Value

Number the boxes from 1 to 50.

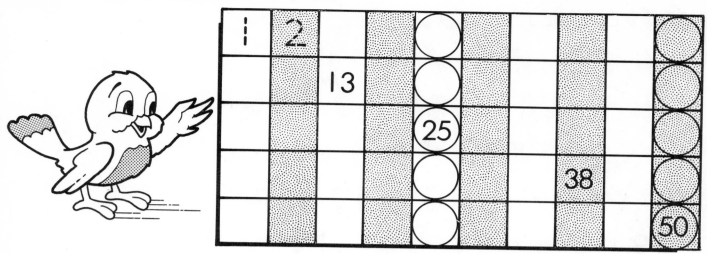

To count by 2s from 2 to 50, write the numerals in the shaded boxes in order.

2 4 __ __ __ __ __ __ __ __

__ __ __ __ __ __ __ __

__ __ __ __ __ __

To count by 5s from 5 to 50, write the numerals in the circled boxes in order.

5 __ __ __ __ __ __ __ __ __

Fill in the boxes by counting by 2s and 5s.

4 ☐ ☐ 10   ☐   ☐ ☐ 24

18 20 ☐ ☐   30

35

20   50

21 Counting & Place Value

Show your path in the zoo. Begin with 0 and count by 5s to 100 in order.

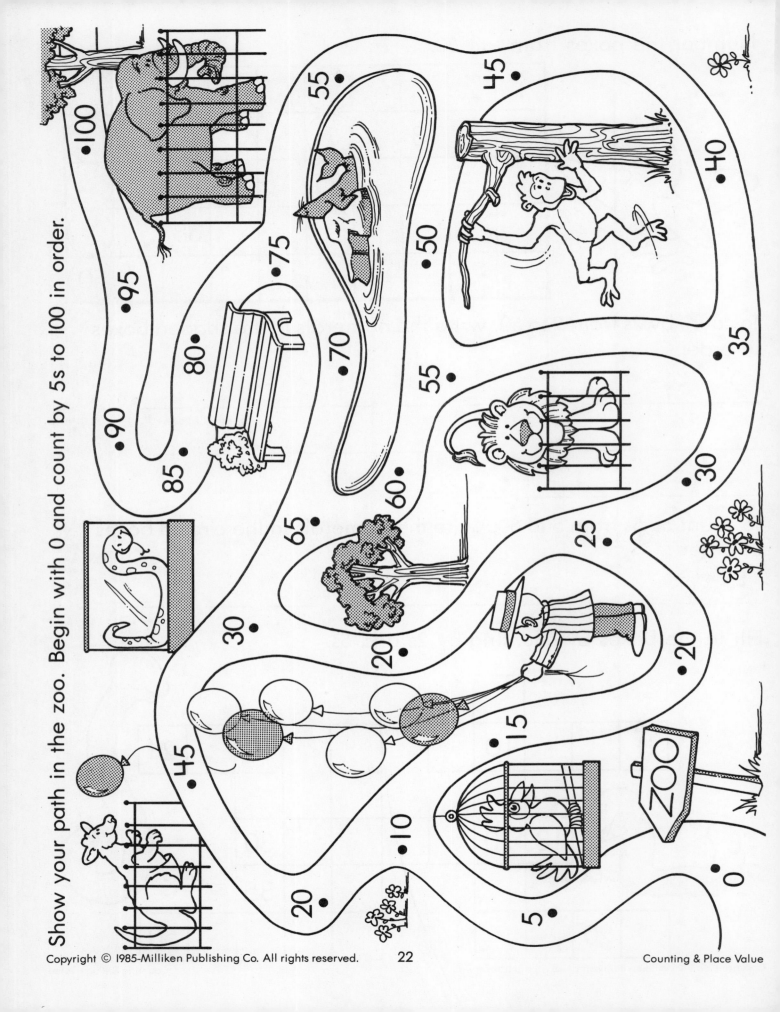

22

Counting & Place Value

Number the path to the roller coaster from 1 to 30.

Write the circled
numerals in order
to count by 3s.

3 ___ ___ ___ ___ ___ ___ ___ ___ ___

23

Counting & Place Value

Count the sets. Compare them.

is greater than

$$18 > 15$$

is less than

$$15 < 18$$

___ > ___

___ < ___

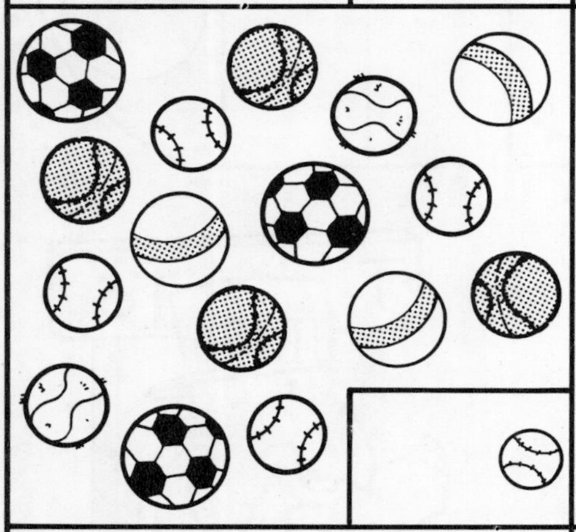

___ > ___

___ < ___

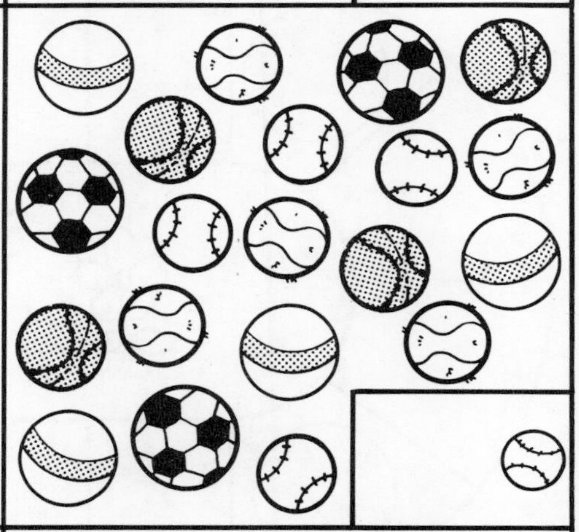

___ > ___

___ < ___

24

Counting & Place Value

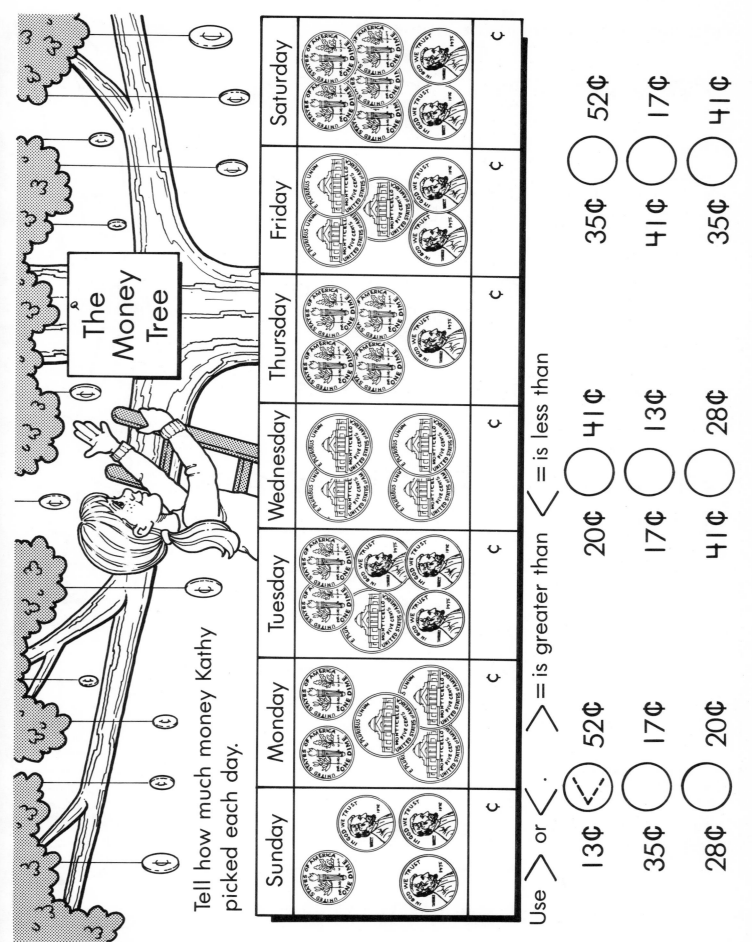

The Money Tree

Tell how much money Kathy picked each day.

Sunday	Monday	Tuesday	Wednesday	Thursday	Friday	Saturday
¢	¢	¢	¢	¢	¢	¢

Use $>$ or $<$. $>$ = is greater than $<$ = is less than

13¢ $\bigcirc$ 52¢   20¢ $\bigcirc$ 41¢   35¢ $\bigcirc$ 52¢

35¢ $\bigcirc$ 17¢   17¢ $\bigcirc$ 13¢   41¢ $\bigcirc$ 17¢

28¢ $\bigcirc$ 20¢   41¢ $\bigcirc$ 28¢   35¢ $\bigcirc$ 41¢

25

Counting & Place Value

Find the pattern. Write the numerals.

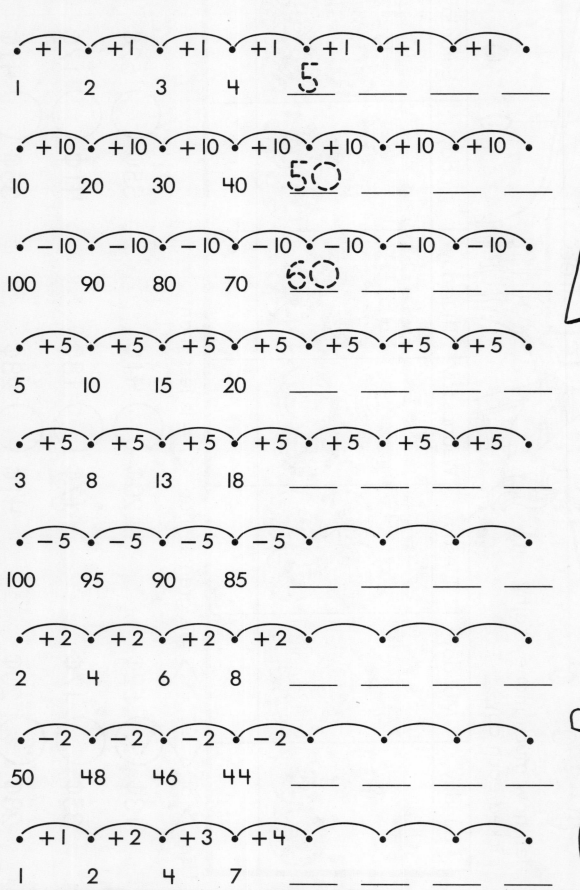

+1 +1 +1 +1 +1 +1 +1
1   2   3   4   5   ___ ___ ___

+10 +10 +10 +10 +10 +10 +10
10   20   30   40   50   ___ ___ ___

−10 −10 −10 −10 −10 −10 −10
100   90   80   70   60   ___ ___ ___

+5 +5 +5 +5 +5 +5 +5
5   10   15   20   ___ ___ ___ ___

+5 +5 +5 +5 +5 +5 +5
3   8   13   18   ___ ___ ___ ___

−5 −5 −5 −5
100   95   90   85   ___ ___ ___ ___

+2 +2 +2 +2
2   4   6   8   ___ ___ ___ ___

−2 −2 −2 −2
50   48   46   44   ___ ___ ___ ___

+1 +2 +3 +4
1   2   4   7   ___ ___ ___ ___

   26   Counting & Place Value

Follow the patterns. Write the numerals.

3 13 23 33 __ __ __ __ __ __ 93

5 15 25 __ __ __ __ __ __ __ 95

8 18 28 __ __ __ __ __ __ __ 98

2 12 22 __ __ __ __ __ __ __ 92

10 20 30 __ __ __ __ __ __ __ 100

6 16 26 __ __ __ __ __ __ __ 96

2 4 6 __ __ __ __ __ __ __ 20

1 3 5 __ __ __ __ __ __ __ 19

5 10 15 20 __ __ __ __ __ __ 50

4 9 14 19 __ __ __ __ __ __ 49

Counting & Place Value

Cross out the numeral that does not belong.

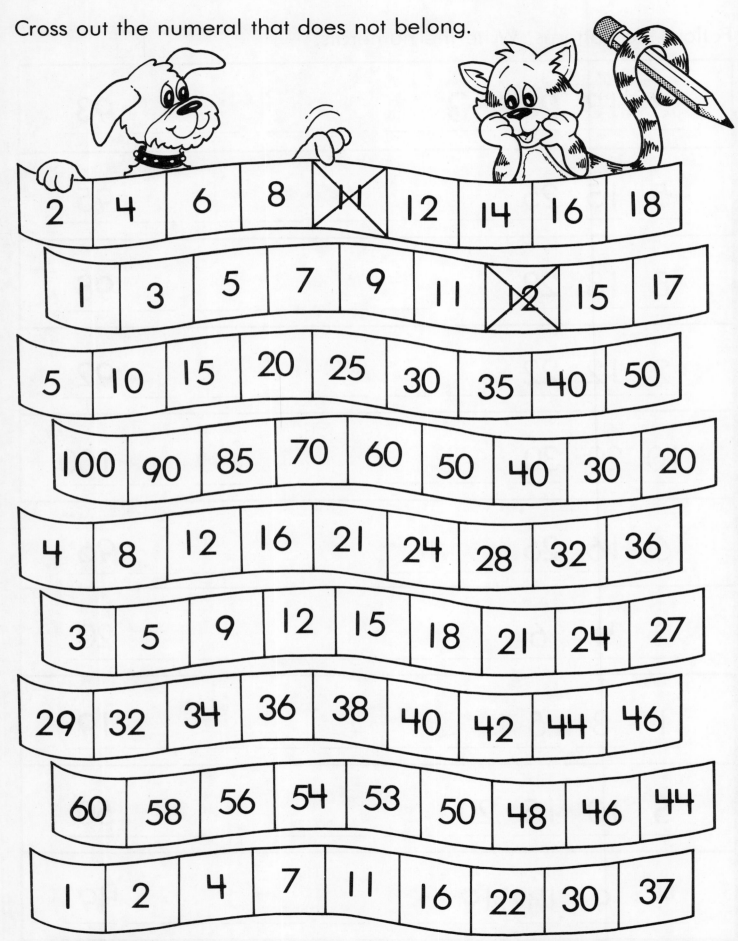

| 2 | 4 | 6 | 8 | ~~11~~ | 12 | 14 | 16 | 18 |

| 1 | 3 | 5 | 7 | 9 | 11 | ~~12~~ | 15 | 17 |

| 5 | 10 | 15 | 20 | 25 | 30 | 35 | 40 | 50 |

| 100 | 90 | 85 | 70 | 60 | 50 | 40 | 30 | 20 |

| 4 | 8 | 12 | 16 | 21 | 24 | 28 | 32 | 36 |

| 3 | 5 | 9 | 12 | 15 | 18 | 21 | 24 | 27 |

| 29 | 32 | 34 | 36 | 38 | 40 | 42 | 44 | 46 |

| 60 | 58 | 56 | 54 | 53 | 50 | 48 | 46 | 44 |

| 1 | 2 | 4 | 7 | 11 | 16 | 22 | 30 | 37 |

   Counting & Place Value